Mission Statement

You are the hero of this mission.

Each section of this book is numbered. At the end of most sections, you will have to make a choice. The choice you make will take you to a different section of the book.

Some of your choices will help you to complete your mission successfully. But if you make the wrong choice, death may be the best you can hope for! Because even that is better than being UNDEAD and becoming a slave of the monsters you have sworn to destroy!

Dare you go up against a world of monsters?

All right, then.

Let's see what you've got...

Introduction

You are an agent of **G.H.O.S.T.** — Global Headquarters Opposing Supernatural Threats.

Our world is under constant attack by supernatural horrors that lurk in the shadows. It's your job to make sure they stay there.

You have studied all kinds of monsters, and know their habits and behaviour. You are an expert in disguise, able to move among monsters in human form as a spy. You are expert in all forms of martial arts. G.H.O.S.T. has supplied you with weapons, equipment and other assets that make you capable of destroying any supernatural creature.

G.H.O.S.T.

You are based at Arcane Hall, a spooky mansion. Your butler, Cranberry, is another G.H.O.S.T. agent who assists you in your adventures, providing you with information and backup.

Your life at Arcane Hall is comfortable and peaceful; but you know that at any moment, the G.H.O.S.T. High Command can order you into action in any part of the world...

1

You and Cranberry have been sent to Sydney, Australia.

You are sitting in a café by the famous Opera House, waiting for the Director General of G.H.O.S.T. to contact you about the mission.

"Any idea why we are here?" you ask Cranberry.

"I'm afraid I'm as much in the dark as you about this one, Agent," he replies. "Ultra Top Secret, Code Magneta — the highest level of operation there is at G.H.O.S.T."

"I hate waiting," you say. "I just wish something would happen."

At that very moment there is a thunderous noise. You look across the harbour to see a huge creature, half-man, half-amphibian, emerging from the water. It lets out a roar that sends a huge wave crashing against the ferry dock.

"You really should be more careful about what you wish for," says Cranberry.

To try and find out what type of Monster you're dealing with, go to 17.

To attack the creature immediately, go to 36.

2

"Give me the BAM, now!" you order Alpha.

But before she can pass you the weapon, Dr Omega shouts, "Stop them!"

The two mutants rush at you and Alpha and smash you both to the floor.

Dr Omega glares at you. She points at Alpha. "Deal with this traitor. And as for you, let's see what your weapon does to you."

She aims your BAM (Blast All Monsters) at you and pulls the trigger. It is the last thing you ever see.

Your BAM weapon blasts all monsters and it turns out that it blasts Monster Hunters too! Go back to 1.

3

"I'm sure that Dr Omega will have heard about the destruction of the mutant in the harbour. It's my guess that they know we'll be coming. Let's just land and see if we can negotiate with her."

Suddenly, the jet's anti-missile warning sounds and the computer's voice rings out. "INCOMING!"

You look out of the window to see two huge

fireballs heading your way.

"Where have they come from?" you gasp.

"This is no time to ask questions, Agent," warns Cranberry. "We need to avoid them!"

To use the autopilot to avoid the fireballs, go to 15.

To fly the jet yourself, go to 19.

You wake up to find yourself strapped to a bed. Bright lights shine in your eyes. You realise that you are in some sort of operating theatre. A figure holding a syringe walks into view.

"Dr Omega," you whisper.

"Don't worry, Agent," she says, "this won't hurt. You are privileged, I am going to mix a few extra-special DNA strands into your body. Welcome to the world of mutants!"

You feel the needle enter your arm and then nothing...

The future doesn't look good for you! Go back to 1.

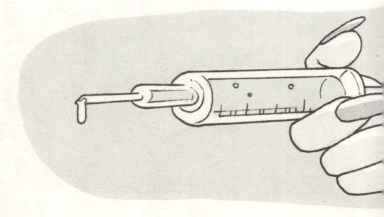

5

Keeping an eye on the mutant, you wait for Cranberry and the Spook Truck. Within minutes the truck screeches to a halt and you quickly unpack the MUM.

"We're dealing with a mutant," you tell Cranberry. "We need to get close enough to use the MUM to scramble up the mutant's DNA and destroy it."

"And how do you propose to do that?" asks Cranberry.

To follow the mutant in the Spook Truck, go to 49.

To find a boat, go to 43.

6

You grab the MUM weapon from Alpha's hand. The two rhino-mutants rush towards you but you're too quick for them. You pull the trigger and they disappear in a wisp of smoke.

You turn to Dr Omega. "Put the syringe down," you say.

"I don't think so," replies the doctor. She emits a low growl and you gasp in horror as

she transforms into a creature from your worst
nightmares! She is a mutant!

Before you can react, Dr Omega smashes the
MUM from your grasp. The weapon spins across
the floor.

**To try and reach the MUM weapon,
go to 16.**

**To ask Alpha to grab the MUM weapon and
use it, go to 11.**

**To plead with Dr Omega to spare you,
go to 32.**

7

"We need to get out of here," you tell Cranberry. "Put your parachute on and get ready to eject."

Seconds later you hit the eject button. You and Cranberry are shot out of the stricken jet as it plummets to the ground. As your parachute opens, you see the mutant turning around to attack. It opens its mouth, ready to spit out another stream of fire.

To reach for your BAM weapon, go to 24.

To use your MUM weapon, go to 44.

"What is the mission?" you ask.

"We need you to get into the institute, link up with our contact and work with them to find out what Dr Omega's plans are and stop them."

"Nothing simple then," you say.

"That's why it's a Code Magneta mission and why you've been chosen," the DG replies. "This mutant in the harbour seems to suggest that Dr Omega's plans are already under way, so you need to get there quickly. The co-ordinates of the institute have been sent to you. Good luck, Agent." The comms link closes.

Cranberry looks up the co-ordinates. "Hmmm. The institute is in the outback. Some 1500 miles north-west of here. How do you want to get there?"

To take the Spook Truck, go to 39.

To fly out in the G.H.O.S.T. jet, go to 28.

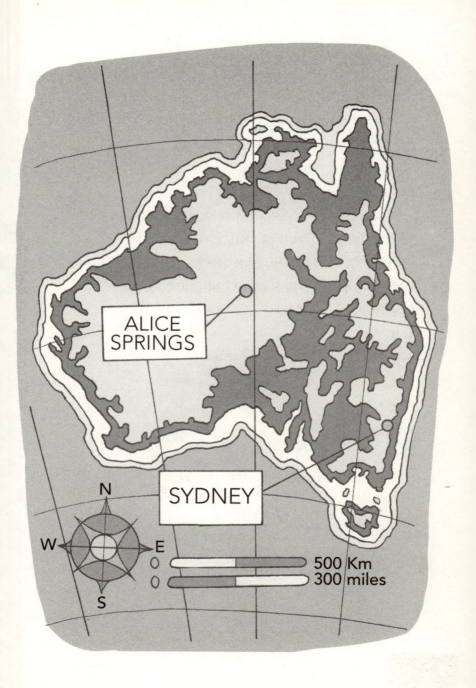

"Dr Omega, I presume," you say.

The woman shakes her head. "No. I am Alpha. You may have heard of me."

You smile. "You're the insider the DG told me about."

Alpha nods. "I've been worried about what Dr Omega has been planning, which is why I contacted G.H.O.S.T. She seems more interested in creating monsters than helping to cure diseases."

You tell her about the mutants you have had to fight in the past few hours.

"There are more of these creatures," replies Alpha. "Dr Omega has accelerated a breeding programme. There are two dozen newly-created mutants in the incubator room. It's only a matter of hours before she starts to let them free."

"Where's Cranberry?" you ask.

"He has been taken to the operating theatre. I fear that he is going to become part of this programme." She points to a bag. "Your weapons are in there. I told the doctor that I needed to analyse them. She believed me. I'll do what I can to help, but there isn't much time to stop her."

To try and rescue Cranberry, go to 18.

If you want to find Dr Omega, go to 40.

10

You continue to blast away at the monster, but the shots still have no effect. The creature smashes its giant hands down on the water, sending a huge wave towards you.

You turn to run, but you are too late. A wall of water hits you, flinging your body against the roof of the opera house. Thankfully, the pain is short-lived as you pass into blackness and drop to the ground, dead.

There are no encores for you! Go back to 1.

11

"Use the MUM!" you cry.

Alpha rushes to the weapon, picks it up and points it at Dr Omega.

The doctor laughs. "You are one of us. You are a mutant."

Alpha shakes her head. "I'm not like you. I believe that everyone should live together in peace."

"Don't be foolish," says the doctor. "I forgive your treacherous behaviour. Put the gun down."

Dr Omega suddenly leaps at Alpha, but you are too quick for her. You also leap forward and grab the MUM from Alpha's hand. You take aim at the doctor and pull the trigger.

A beam of protons hits Dr Omega. With a scream, she disappears.

Go to 50.

12

"I'll parachute in," you decide. You put on your drop suit and load a weapons bag with the BAM gun and MUM device.

"Two minutes until target," warns Cranberry. He reduces speed to allow you to parachute down without being sucked into the plane's engines.

You stand on the ejection plate. "Go!" you order. Part of the roof snaps open and you are ejected out of the plane.

Go to 41.

13

You move a chair to the heating grille and climb. You grab hold of it to try and force it open. As you touch the grille there is a huge crack as an electric current surges through your body. You are thrown to the floor and pass out.

Go to 4.

14

You arrive within range of the mutant and take aim with the MUM. Pulling the trigger, you send out a beam of protons that hit the mutant's back.

Instantly, the mutant seems to come apart in front of your eyes as its DNA unscrambles. Then there is a huge explosion and nothing remains of the mutant other than wisps of smoke drifting across the harbour waters.

Go to 46.

You hit the autopilot and the jet banks violently to the right, narrowly avoiding the fireballs.

"Look, Agent!" You turn and see Cranberry pointing out of the window. You follow his pointing finger and gasp in amazement — a dragon-like creature hovers in the sky in front of you. It opens its mouth and another fireball erupts. Before the autopilot can react to this latest attack, the fireball hits the wing, incinerating the engine.

Another fireball heads your way. It is the last thing you see as the plane is engulfed by the deadly blast.

Never trust a machine when you can do the job yourself! Go back to 1.

16

The doctor throws you to the ground. Alpha tries to run from the room, but the doctor lashes out and she crashes to the floor.

"Yes, I am a mutant!" rasps Dr Omega. "I will change this world and the puny humans in it. And you will be part of it."

She picks up the syringe and plunges the needle into your arm. You pass out, knowing that you are going to become a mutant!

You weren't expecting that! Go back to 1.

17

"Get the Spook Truck while I try and find out what this thing is," you tell Cranberry.

He hurries away as you reach into your holdall and pull out your MAAD (Monster and Alien Detector). You point it at the creature and switch it on. Within seconds you have your answer:

MUTANT
HIGHLY DANGEROUS
EXTREME CAUTION
ADVISED

WEAPON : MUM
(MASH UP MONSTERS)

The mutant turns away from you and begins to wade through the water towards the Sydney Harbour Bridge. You realise that the MUM weapon is in the Spook Truck, but the creature is getting away!

To find a boat and try to follow the creature, go to 43.

To wait for the Spook Truck, go to 5.

18

"I need to make sure Cranberry is safe," you say. "Where might he be?"

"He is to be 'operated on' by Dr Omega, and turned into a mutant," replies Alpha.

"What about the other mutants that are here?" you ask.

"They have been brainwashed by the doctor. They think she is right when she tells them that they are better than humans and should take over the world."

"Not you though," you say.

Alpha smiles. "I think I have more human in me than creature. Now, we should go and save your friend. I'll take you to the operating room."

Do I trust her? you think. *Is she different from the other mutants?*

To go with Alpha, go to 38.

To go on your own, go to 29.

19

You grab hold of the controls and bank right to avoid the deadly fireballs. *Where are these coming from?* you wonder.

Your question is answered as you see a nightmare creature flying towards you. It is a half-human and half-dragon mutant! It opens its mouth and spits out another fireball. Again, you steer the plane away from the deadly projectile.

"Switch on missile systems," you order the jet's computer.

"ACTIVATED!"

"Engage enemy," you say. But the creature sends a stream of fireballs towards the jet. You try to avoid them but there are too many to deal with. One of them hits a wing and incinerates the engine. The plane starts to plummet through the sky.

To parachute from the jet, go to 7.

Try to and crash-land the jet, go to 25.

20

You make your way along the corridors. To your surprise, they are empty. There is no one else around.

You eventually arrive at a set of double doors. You open them and step through.

Bright lights snap on, blinding you. A voice sounds out.

"Welcome, Agent! Thank you for joining us! It saved us having to bring you here!"

You feel a blow to your head and you drop to the floor, unconscious.

Go to 4.

You speed towards the creature and open fire with your BAM weapon.

However, the weapon has no impact against the creature. It turns to face you and before you can react, it plucks you from the boat with its huge webbed hands.

Desperately you try to break free, but it is hopeless. Its tongue shoots out, enveloping you and then pulling you towards its cavernous mouth and razor-sharp teeth.

Its jaws snap shut, sending you to oblivion.

Where was your MUM when you needed it? Go back to 1.

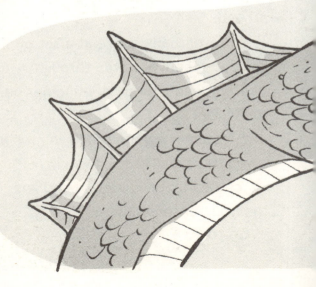

"Why are you doing this?" you ask the doctor.

"I have my reasons," she replies. "Humans are weak. Look at the world they are creating. Famines, wars, environmental destruction. To survive, mankind must become stronger. I have the power to make that happen."

You move closer towards Dr Omega. If you don't neutralise her quickly, she will turn Cranberry into a mutant — and he's weird enough already!

"I've heard that before from all sorts of monsters," you reply. "And do you know what, humans always seem to come out on top. And anyway, you're human too! You're part of the problem."

"No," replies the doctor. "I'm part of the solution!"

To tell Alpha to pass you the BAM weapon, go to 2.

To grab hold of the MUM weapon, go to 6.

To use your martial arts skills on Dr Omega, go to 42.

"Tell me more about this doctor," you say.

"Dr Alexis Omega is a brilliant scientist. Her area of research is DNA, the genetic code that makes up the characteristics of all living things. She wanted to explore how human DNA could be changed to help to eliminate all disorders and diseases. But during her work on these structures, she stumbled across a process of how she could mix human and non-human DNA together. Not only that, she discovered how to speed up growth. Babies grew into adults in months. Some of these mutants could take on the form of other creatures at will and they developed superhuman powers."

"That sounds incredible," you say.

"However," continues the DG, "some of her 'experiments' didn't work. Monsters were created, she was thrown out of her university and her research was shelved. Instead of giving up on her work, she founded the Institute of Human Potential, where she continues her experiments."

If you have already found out about the Institute of Human Potential, go to 8.

If you haven't, go to 33.

24

You reach for your BAM weapon and take careful aim as the mutant once again heads towards you. You blast the creature and score a direct hit.

However, it continues to fly towards you. Again you shoot, but this creature is too powerful! You throw away the BAM and fumble for the MUM weapon instead, but it is too late. The mutant opens its mouth and spits a stream of fire at you. You feel the burning heat and then, thankfully, nothing more.

Wrong choice, Agent! Go back to 1 and start again.

25

"I'm going to try and land this thing," you tell Cranberry. "Hold on!"

You struggle with the controls, trying desperately to avoid a fatal crash. Again the mutant attacks, sending another fireball at you. It hits the jet and explodes, sending you and Cranberry to oblivion.

When the going gets hot, get out of the kitchen! Go back to 1.

26

You report back to the Director General of G.H.O.S.T. on your comms link. She is not impressed with you.

"You let the mutant get away?" She looks grim-faced. "You're obviously not good enough for this mission. I'll find another agent who is up to the task. Return home immediately." The link goes dead.

Harsh but fair — you weren't good enough! Go back to 1.

You leap towards the woman but suddenly find yourself flying backwards as she spins around and catches you with a perfect kick to the chest. You crash into a table sending computer screens and glass bottles everywhere. The woman moves towards you as you struggle to your feet, ready for the oncoming attack.

"I do hope you're going to be sensible and calm down," she says.

Go to 9.

28

"Driving will take too long," you say. "Let's get to the airport and take the G.H.O.S.T. Phantom Flyer."

Soon you and Cranberry are flying towards the Institute for Human Potential. Cranberry checks out possible landing sites near the institute. "There's a dry lake nearby we could land on," he informs you. "But our arrival won't go unnoticed. Do you want to parachute in and try and make your way into the institute without being spotted?"

If you want to parachute in, go to 12.

If you want to land near the institute, go to 3.

29

"Don't worry, I'll find Cranberry on my own."

"Don't you trust me?" replies Alpha. "Perhaps Dr Omega is right about humans — they are weak and selfish beings."

To change your mind, go to 38.

To go on your own, go to 20.

30

You open the throttle until the engine is at full power. The mutant continues its journey through the harbour waters, sweeping boats aside with its huge webbed hands.

You realise it is heading for the Harbour Bridge. Hundreds of vehicles and thousands of people are in danger — you have to act immediately!

To use your BAM weapon, go to 21.

To use the MUM, go to 14.

31

"Who are you?" you ask.

"I am one of Dr Omega's assistants," she replies. "I am known as Beta."

"Well, as we're expected, let's not disappoint Dr Omega," you reply. "How do we get to the institute?"

The woman holds out her hand and a kaleidoscope of stars envelops you and Cranberry. You feel as though your body is being ripped into a million pieces. Then the feeling passes and you find yourself alone in a large white room. Your weapons and comms link have gone and there is no sign of Beta or Cranberry.

To try and escape from the room immediately, go to 13.

To wait for someone to enter the room, and then try and escape, go to 45.

32

Dr Omega moves towards you.

"You don't have to do this!" you say. "I'm sure we can sort something out!"

"Don't worry, I'm going to sort it all out by myself!" snarls Dr Omega. "It is the end for you and all humans. I will create a new race to inhabit the world!"

To try and run out of the room, go to 16.

Get Alpha to use the MUM weapon, go to 11.

33

"Tell me about the Institute of Human Potential," you say.

"This establishment is where Dr Omega continues her work into the development of mutating humans into superhuman creatures," replies the DG. "It is situated in the Australian outback, miles from anywhere. G.H.O.S.T. has been monitoring this facility for some time. We have an insider in the institute, code name Agent Alpha. Alpha is a volunteer and has refused to reveal his or her identity. We don't even know if

Alpha is mutant or human."

"What has this agent reported?" you ask.

"They claim that Dr Omega wishes to unleash her mutant army on the world and take revenge on those that stopped her research."

You shake your head. "Why do rejected scientists always seem to go off the rails? It's like something out of a movie or a comic book!"

If you have already found out about Dr Omega go to 8.

If you haven't, go to 23.

34

You head towards the research lab through the corridors of the institute. To your surprise there is no one else around.

You finally reach the laboratory and step inside. You see a woman staring into a microscope. She has human form but the skin and eyes of a lizard.

Without looking up, she begins speaking to you. "Welcome, Agent. I've been expecting you."

To question her, go to 9.

To use your martial arts fighting skills, go to 27.

35

"I don't think so," you say and grab hold of your BAM weapon.

But before you can use it, the woman holds out her hand towards you and the BAM flies from your grip. She stares at you and you feel your senses slipping away. You are helpless to fight against the power of her mind! Gasping for breath, you are forced to your knees before passing out into blackness.

Go to 4.

36

You reach into your holdall and pull out your BAM weapon.

"Are you sure that's a good idea?" asks Cranberry. "We don't know what sort of monster it is."

"I'm not waiting around for a polite introduction," you reply and run to the quayside. You take aim with your BAM and shoot at the creature, but it is too far away and your shots have no effect. The monster turns towards you.

"I really do think we should find out what

we're dealing with here," warns Cranberry.

If you wish to continue to attack the monster, go to 10.

To take Cranberry's advice, go to 17.

37

"Cranberry, I could do with some help here!" you cry into the comms link.

"I can see that," he replies. "On my way."

The creature banks again and heads towards you. However, at that moment, the jet zaps the mutant. The creature spins away, chases down the jet and sends a fireball towards it.

You stare in horror as the jet is hit.

"Cranberry, get out of there!" you yell into the radio. You sigh with relief as Cranberry ejects from the doomed plane. His parachute opens and he drifts towards the ground.

But you have no time to waste as the mutant banks again and closes in for the kill!

To reach for your BAM weapon, go to 24.

To use your MUM weapon, go to 44.

38

"Show me where to go," you say. You reach for your weapons.

"No," replies Alpha, "I will hold them and pretend that I have captured you."

Again, you wonder if you can trust her.

You head down the corridors of the institute, passing other strange-looking mutants. They stand aside to let Alpha escort you.

Eventually you reach the operations room and enter. You see Cranberry strapped to a bed. Dr Omega stands over him, holding a syringe. Two mutants stand either side of her. They are a cross between a human and a rhino.

"I have re-captured the Agent," says Alpha.

"Good work!" smiles the doctor. "Welcome, Agent! You're just in time to see your friend enter the world of mutants. And then it will be your turn," she adds.

To attack Dr Omega immediately, go to 2.

To talk to her and buy some time, go to 22.

39

"The jet will take time to get ready, let's set off now in the Spook Truck."

"But that will take hours," says Cranberry.

"Then let's get going!" You set off.

After many hours of driving, a comms message comes in from the DG.

"Dr Omega has launched an all-out attack with the mutants. You're too late!"

What were you thinking? A great agent gets on with the job IMMEDIATELY! Go back to 1.

40

"I'm afraid Cranberry will have to look after himself," you say grimly. "Dr Omega must be stopped. Where will I find her?"

"Probably in her office or the incubator room," Alpha replies.

To head to the incubator room, go to 20.
To head for Dr Omega's office, go to 48.

41

Your parachute opens and you drift down towards the institute.

But before you can land, you see a creature flying towards you. As it gets nearer you can only stare in horror. It is a half-human and half-dragon mutant!

You wonder how dangerous it is. It opens its mouth and spits out a huge fireball.

"Well," you think, "that answers that question!"

You pull on your parachute strings to change direction and just manage to avoid the deadly projectile.

To reach for your MUM weapon, go to 47.
To radio Cranberry for help, go to 37.

42

You leap at Dr Omega and knock the syringe from her hand. The two mutants rush to her rescue, but you hold the doctor in a headlock.

"Tell them to back off," you order.

"I don't think so," says the doctor. "I think it's time to meet the real me!"

She begins to transform into a monster from your worst nightmares. Dr Omega is a mutant!

Go to 16.

43

You race along the quayside and find a speedboat with a high-powered outboard motor. Releasing the mooring ropes, you jump in and hotwire the ignition. The engine bursts into life and you head out into the harbour, chasing down the mutant.

If you waited for the Spook Truck, go to 30.
If you didn't, go to 21.

44

Before the mutant can blast you with a fireball, you grab hold of your MUM weapon, take aim and fire. The creature is caught in a beam of protons, which unscramble its DNA. Within seconds all that remains is smoke.

A couple of minutes later you land and join Cranberry. "That was a close one, Agent!" he says. "These mutants are becoming tiresome."

At that moment the air shimmers and you gasp as a woman with the head of an ape suddenly appears from out of thin air!

"Hello, Agent. Hello, Cranberry," she says. "Dr Omega is expecting you. Please follow me."

To attack this person, go to 35.
To do as they say, go to 31.

45

You decide to wait for someone (or something) to come and fetch you and plan your escape.

Sometime later, the door opens and a young man steps inside. He sees you lying on the floor, moaning.

"What is wrong?" he asks. In an instant you leap up and before he can respond, you knock him out with a blow to the head. You move to the door and, making sure no one else is around, step out into the corridor.

There is a sign on the wall. Where should you head to?

To head to the Operation Theatre, go to 20.

To head to the Research Laboratory, go to 34.

46

You head back to shore to meet Cranberry in the Spook Truck.

"Well done, Agent," says Cranberry. "I've set up a comms link with the DG so that you can report back on this incident."

You click on the comms link and the Director General of G.H.O.S.T. appears. You tell her about the mutant.

"Then our worst fears are confirmed," she replies. "I sent you to Australia because we have had some disturbing reports about the Institute of Human Potential run by Dr Alexis Omega."

To find out more about Dr Omega, go to 23.

To find out more about the Institute of Human Potential, go to 33.

47

As the mutant creature banks around, you fumble desperately for your MUM weapon.

But it is too late, the creature is once again upon you. It opens its jaws and you feel the blistering heat as a fireball heads your way. You pull on the parachute strings again but you are helpless. The ball of fire engulfs the parachute and you plummet downwards to your end.

That creature was just too hot to handle! Go back to 1.

You grab your weapons bag and head out of the laboratory. You follow the signs towards Dr Omega's office.

As you turn a corner you see two wolf-like figures escorting Cranberry towards Dr Omega's office.

"Cranberry!" you shout.

The mutants spin around, but you are ready for them. You blast them with your MUM and they disappear into wisps of smoke.

You run towards Cranberry. "Are you all right?" you ask.

"Oh perfectly," replies Cranberry. You cry out in horror as his body transforms into a huge boa constrictor and coils around you. You are helpless to do anything as your former friend crushes the life out of you.

Turns out Cranberry was a snake in the grass! Go back to 1.

49

"We'll follow it in the Spook Truck," you tell Cranberry. "It's heading towards the Harbour Bridge so we can head it off there."

You set off, but the Sydney traffic is heavy and you soon lose sight of the mutant.

Finally, you reach the Harbour Bridge, but there is no sign of the mutant — just a trail of carnage and devastation.

"I think you should inform G.H.O.S.T. High Command about this," says Cranberry.

Go to 26.

50

Alpha smiles. "Thank you. It's true I'm not like her. Just because we are different, we don't have to behave badly."

You nod in agreement.

"What will you do about the rest of us mutants? Will you use the MUM?" asks Alpha.

You shake your head. "I think you'll be able to convince them that they can live in harmony with humankind. Dr Omega was named after the last letter of the Greek alphabet. You're Alpha, the first letter. Maybe you're the start of a new era!"

"Agent! What's happening?"

You turn to see Cranberry trying to struggle free. "What am I doing here? Did I miss anything?"

You laugh. "It's a long story, Cranberry..."

"I suppose you saved the world again?"

"I suppose I did," you reply. "I'll tell you all about it on the way home..."

Phantom Flyer: For fast international and intercontinental travel, you use the Phantom Flyer, a supersonic business jet crammed full of detection and communication equipment and weaponry.

Spook Truck: For more local travel you use one of G.H.O.S.T.'s fleet of Spook Trucks — heavily armed and armoured SUVs you requisition from local agents.

MAAD (Monster and Alien Detector)

BAM (Blasts All Monsters)

MUM (Mash Up Mutants)

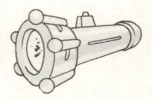

EDGE

I HERO

MONSTER HUNTER

WEREWOLF

STEVE BARLOW ◆ STEVE SKIDMORE

Illustrated by PAUL DAVIDSON

You are an agent of **G.H.O.S.T.** — Global
Headquarters Opposing Supernatural Threats.

1

Cranberry's voice crackles in your ear. "How's the
trip going?"

You stare out of the windscreen of the hired
Lada 4x4. "I never want to see snow, cabbage
soup or birch trees, ever again."

"Sorry," says Cranberry cheerfully, "but the
Russian Government doesn't like G.H.O.S.T."

"So no Phantom Flyer and no Spook Truck? All
I've got is a few bits of basic equipment that
are not going to be much help if I have to fight
werewolves..."

Continue the adventure in:

About the 2Steves

"The 2Steves" are
Britain's most popular
writing double act
for young people,
specialising in comedy
and adventure. They
perform regularly in schools and libraries,
and at festivals, taking the power of words
and story to audiences of all ages.

Together they have written many books,
including the *I HERO Immortals* and *iHorror* series.

About the illustrator:
Paul Davidson

Paul Davidson is a British
illustrator and comic book artist.